The PUZZLE BOOK

Delightfully Delicious Brain Teasers for the Entire Family

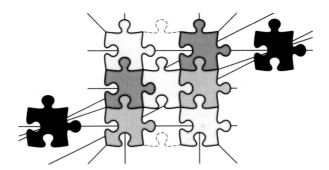

THE GRABARCHUK FAMILY

Mud Puddle inc.
NEW YORK

The Puzzle Book:
Delightfully Delicious Brain Teasers
for the Entire Family
by The Grabarchuk Family

Copyright © 2012 by Mud Puddle, Inc.

Published by:
Mud Puddle, Inc.
36 W. 25th Street
New York, NY 10010
info@mudpuddleinc.com

ISBN: 978-1-60311-377-9

Printed in China, April 2018

5 7 9 10 8 6 4

Contents

Introduction

Our newest puzzle collection features a puzzling diversity designed to test and train your solving skills and please your imagination. The main tools required to solve these puzzles are logical reasoning and insight; however, some puzzles will require elementary math.

The puzzles in this book include both manipulative and non-manipulative types. The manipulative ones are traditional and are represented by coin, matchstick, folding and assembling puzzles. The non-manipulative puzzles embrace visual, logical, spatial, pencil-and-paper, arithmetical, geometric and word challenges.

The book consists of two parts: Puzzles and Solutions. The rules for each puzzle are detailed and refined to the extent that they are simple to understand, the goals are clear and any potential ambiguity is avoided as much as possible. Solutions, at the end of the book, present detailed diagrams for each puzzle with additional explanations where necessary.

Last but not least, we would like to express our gratitude to all members of our big puzzle family for their constant inspiration, support and valuable feedback. We do believe every solver will find challenges to his or her taste in this collection and will have hours of clever amusement. You can drop us a line about your solving experience and respective findings at grabarchukpuzzles@gmail.com.

Happy Puzzling!

The Grabarchuk Family
Uzhgorod, Ukraine
May 2012

1 ▼ Four Jigsaw Pieces

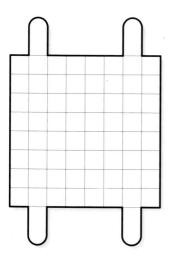

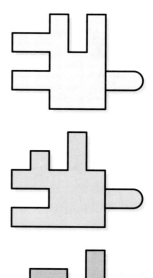

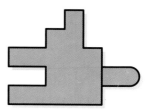

▼ Show how the four jigsaw pieces with handles can form the shape shown. You can rotate the pieces and flip them over, but they cannot overlap.

2 ▼ The Eyes

▼ Find two pairs of identical eyes.

3 ▼ Three to the Height

▼ Four matchsticks create the number
  3. Move 2 matchsticks to create as
  large a 2-digit number as possible.

4 ▼ Three-in-Cells

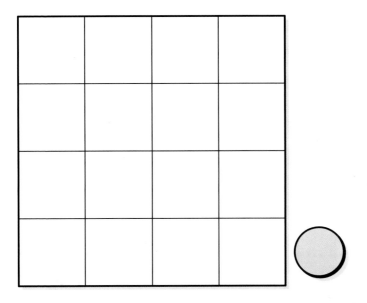

▼ How many coins can be
placed in the cells of the 4 x 4
grid (one coin per cell) so that
in each row, column and each
of the two main diagonals
there are exactly 3 coins?

5 ▼ Square Paper Frame

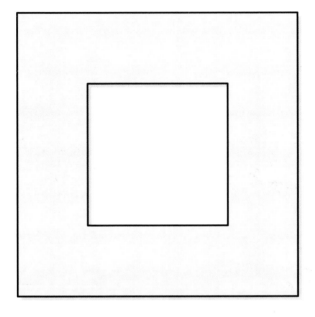

▼ The square paper frame is colored on one side and white on the other. The outer size of the frame is 1 x 1; the hole is 0.5 x 0.5. Fold the frame into another square frame of the same proportions, but now with both of its sides (face and back) fully colored. Make the new frame the largest size possible with the fewest consecutive folds.

6 ▼ Keychain

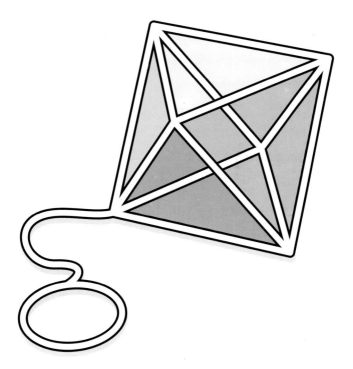

▼ By traveling along the bold white lines, draw the entire 3-D shape of the keychain in one continuous line without ever drawing any of its parts twice.

7 ▼ Make the Sun

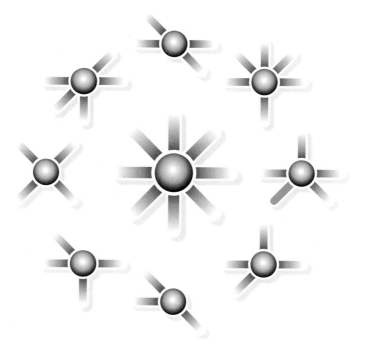

▼ Which two (and only two!)
different fragments, when
stacked together, create the
Sun shown in the center? You
may rotate each fragment as
you like, but you may not
flip it over.

8 ▼ Next Solid

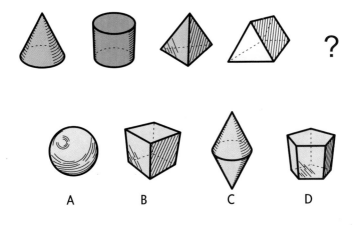

A   B   C   D

▼ In the sequence above, which
solid from the bottom row should
replace the question mark?

9 ▼ Gears

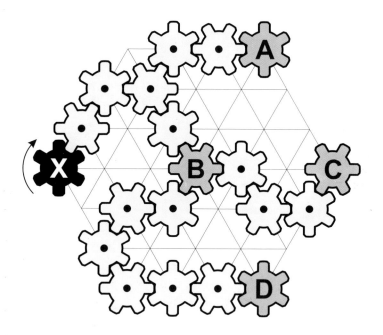

▼ When you turn gear X clockwise,
which two of the lettered gears
(A-D) will also turn clockwise?

10 ▼ DomiDice

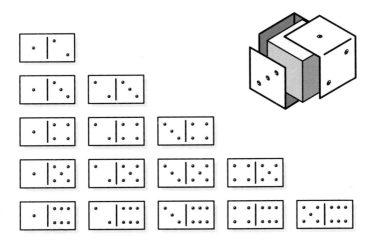

▼ You have five wooden cubes (1 x 1 x 1) and a set of 15 paper, one-sided dominoes (1 x 2), as shown. Each domino may be folded along its middle line and pasted on two adjacent faces of a cube. This way, three folded dominoes can create a die with pips on its faces, like that shown in the diagram. How many dice with the full set of pips (1 to 6) on each of them can be created simultaneously from the given set of dominoes? It's not necessary for the dice to be exactly equal, but each pair of their opposite faces must add up to 7, like in a regular die.

11 ▼ Seven Flowers

▼ You have six fragments of flowers and seven circles (each circle represents the center of one flower), as shown. Show how to make seven complete flowers.

12 ▼ Triangles in Grid

▼ How many outlines of equilateral
triangles of all sizes can you count in
the grid? One triangle is already shown.

13 ▼ Four Buttons

▼ Three holes in each button make an equilateral triangle. Arrange the buttons on the page so that their holes form the most squares of different sizes. In each square the centers of four holes are exactly at its corners. You can rotate buttons, but not overlap them.

14 ▼ Block Strip Origami

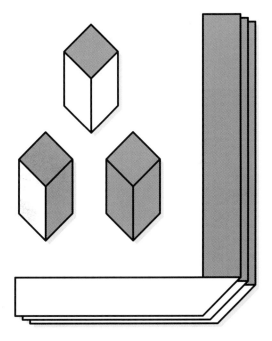

▼ Three single paper origami strips are colored on one side and white on the other. Create three flat, block-like shapes using one strip per shape and folding just one layer of paper at a time. The shapes may have any pattern. Perform as few folds as possible, and use strips as short as you can.

15 ▼ Rolling Wheel

A

B

C

D

▼ The wheel has made one full turn to
the right along a straight line. Which
of the tracks (A-D) did it leave?

16 ▼ Covering a Cube

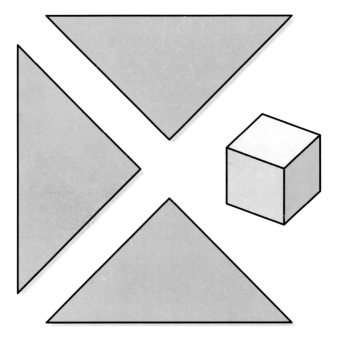

▼ What is the largest cube that can be
covered completely with three equal
right isosceles triangles on a flat,
opaque surface? You cannot fold
or bend the triangles.

17 ▼ Clover Foldcut

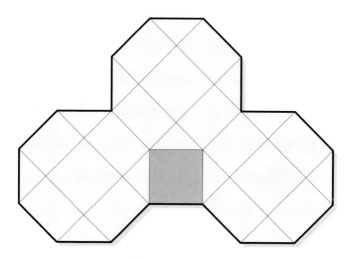

▼ The paper clover shape is formed by three regular octagons and a small square. Make two folds, then two cuts to get four parts of the same area.

18 ▼ Two Coin Squares

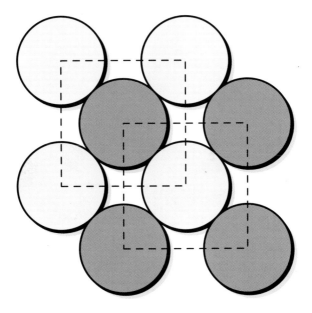

▼ Eight coins form two equal coin squares, light and dark. Now, moving one coin at a time, rearrange the coins to form two *different* coin squares, one of light coins and another of dark ones. Do this in the fewest single coin moves. In its new position, each coin must touch at least two other coins to make a real triangle with them.

19 ▼ Triangle-in-Square

▼ Select two tiles to create a square
with a full perfect equilateral
triangle on it. Tiles can be rotated
but not flipped over or overlapped.

20 ▼ Block-out Knight's Tour

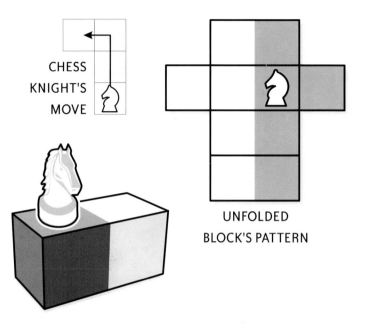

CHESS
KNIGHT'S
MOVE

UNFOLDED
BLOCK'S PATTERN

▼ You have a checkered 1 x 1 x 2 block and a
chess knight on it, as shown. Now, using only
the normal knight's moves (for each move
use an unfolded pattern of the block), have
the knight visit each of the ten cells of the
block's surface exactly once and return to
the initial cell. (A chess knight's move is
shown just above the block.)

Solutions

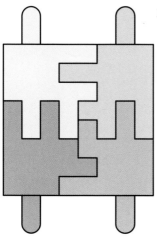

1. Four Jigsaw Pieces

2. The Eyes

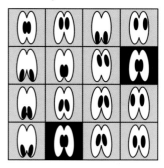

3. Three to the Height

The biggest possible
2-digit number
formed is 77.

4. Three-in-Cells

The solution requires
12 coins, as shown.

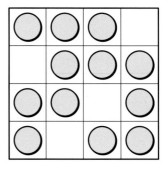

5. Square Paper Frame

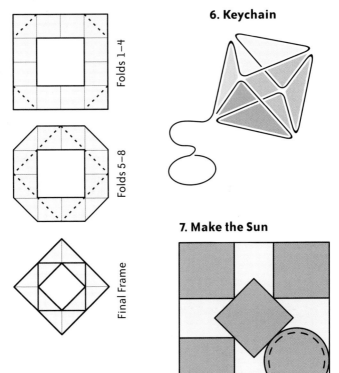

Folds 1–4

Folds 5–8

Final Frame

6. Keychain

7. Make the Sun

8. Next Solid

Each solid in the sequence has a different number of sides (plain or smooth): the cone has 2 sides, the cylinder has 3 sides, the tetrahedron has 4 and the prism has 5. So, to complete the sequence, shape B (cube = 6 sides) replaces the question mark.

B

9. Gears

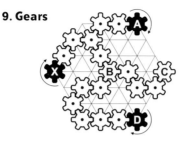

Cube 1

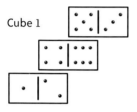

Cube 2

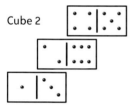

Cube 3

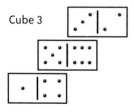

Cube 4

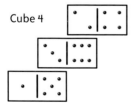

10. DomiDice

We have to eliminate the 1–6, 2–5 and 3–4 dominoes: each of their respective numbers should be on the opposite faces of a die, but, in fact, they can only be on the adjacent faces of the die. Using the remaining 12 dominoes we can create four complete dice. One of the possible combinations is shown.

11. Seven Flowers

12. Triangles in Grid

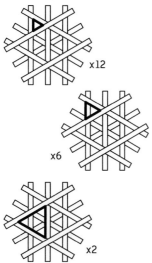

x12

x6

x2

20 equilateral triangles

13. Four Buttons

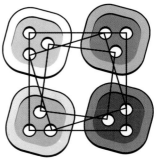

3 different squares

14. Block Strip Origami

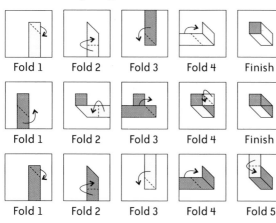

Fold 1   Fold 2   Fold 3   Fold 4   Finish

Fold 1   Fold 2   Fold 3   Fold 4   Finish

Fold 1   Fold 2   Fold 3   Fold 4   Fold 5   Finish

15. Rolling Wheel

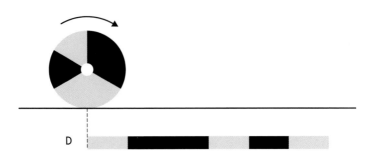

16. Covering a Cube

The biggest cube that can be covered completely with three equal right isosceles triangles on a flat, opaque surface (diagram a) has as its edge of the leg of the triangle (diagram b).

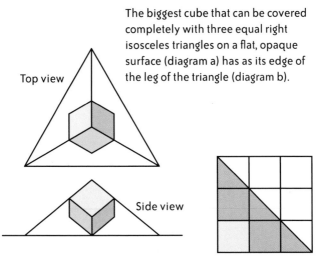

Top view

Side view

Diagram b

17. Clover Foldcut

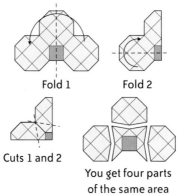

Fold 1　　　　　　Fold 2

Cuts 1 and 2

You get four parts
of the same area

18. Two Coin Squares

Start

Move 1

Move 2

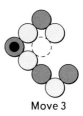

Move 3

Move 4

Move 5

Finish

19. Triangle-in-Square

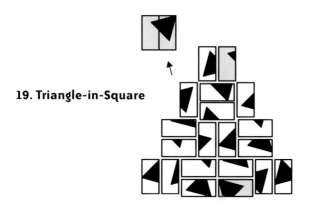

20. Block-out Knight's Tour

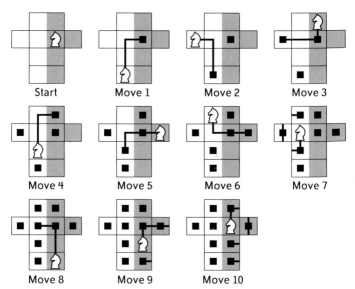